T

# THE OPPOSITE
# OF DEATH

Roberto Saviano

# THE RING

## AND

# THE OPPOSITE OF DEATH

*Translated from the Italian by*
*Abigail Asher*

MACLEHOSE PRESS
QUERCUS · LONDON

"The Ring" was first published in the Italian language in 2007
as *Ragazzi di coca e di camorra* in *L'espresso*.
"The Opposite of Death" was first published *as Il contrario della morte*
in 2007 in the series "I Documenti del Corriere della Sera".
First published in Great Britain in 2013 by MacLehose Press
This paperback edition published in 2014 by

MacLehose Press
an imprint of Quercus
55 Baker Street
7th Floor, South Block
London W1U 8EW

A CIP catalogue record for this book is available
from the British Library.

ISBN (MMP) 978 1 84866 458 6

10 9 8 7 6 5 4 3 2 1

Designed and typeset in Collis by Libanus Press Ltd, Marlborough
Printed and bound in Great Britain by Clays Ltd, St Ives plc

*For Vincenzo and Pietro*
*May the earth hold you lightly*

*You weep only if no-one is looking*
*You cry out only if no-one is there to hear*
*But it is not water, the blood in your veins*
*Carmela Carmé*
*If love is the opposite of death . . .*

"Carmela", Sergio Bruni

*If you must have blood, then give of your own,*
*if it so amuses you.*

Boris Vian

# THE RING

My hands started bothering me the first time I brought a Northern girl to my town. I picked her up at the station, and while I was waiting, I felt a sort of tingling, the kind they say can only be relieved with a slap. I kept scratching my palms, one hand after the other. It must have been nerves. Maybe that's all it was. When the girl got off the train, I put her on the Vespa and tried to get her away as fast as I could, so she wouldn't see where she had just arrived. I don't think that I have ever been ashamed of the place where I grew up, but adolescence presumes to determine what should be savoured and what should be avoided: which areas, and then which locations within those areas, and then even which moments within those locations. I immediately wanted to get to the places I considered worthy of being seen, admired, experienced. The waterfront promenade (turning our backs on the concrete) and the view of the sea (without looking behind us). And then the buffalo calves that are born before the summer begins, making their mothers bellow curses against the pain. Still wet with the caul, the newborn calf looks like it is wearing a cape, the kind of cape that covers the magician in a fairy tale, and under which you can imagine disappearing into the night-time of another world. The only things that might appear beautiful were certain places, moments, things you could only grasp if you concentrated on them and ignored everything else. I accelerated the Vespa, as if to block out the horrors of the backdrop. The girl was too embarrassed to put her arms around my waist, so she tried to find handholds on the saddle, and she even slid her index fingers through the belt-loops of my jeans. She was a Northern girl: she didn't understand that for me – who at the time had never been north of the Cassino line* – such a gesture meant more than if she had just been steadying herself against me. We went into town, and she noticed bunches of flowers scattered in several places on street corners. And even some little lights glowing at ankle height. I wanted to explain what they were. But I did not want to scare her. It would have been uncomfortable to explain that these marked spots where people had been shot, taken out, bumped off. I let her believe that, here too, people drove excessively fast. That, here too, your car could end up wrapped around a tree. Every now and then a plaque appeared on some wall. She came from a city of Resistance fighters and anti-Fascists, so after one backward glance she asked, "Partisans?" She did not know that there had been almost no Resistance movement down here, that the war was an endless slaughter of civilians; that before retreating, the Germans combed the fields and houses, massacring anyone they found. "Yes," I replied,

* Cassino, during the Second World War, was on the Gustav line which separated the south of Italy from the rest of the country.

"Partisans." When I was a kid, I was very good at avoiding certain subjects. Maybe that's why, as I grew up, I felt sort of nauseous about holding them in, and I had to blurt them out to anyone I came across. But, all in all, almost instinctively, I had given her a correct answer. The South is full of plaques in memory of those who died in a different kind of Resistance movement. A Resistance that is harder to describe, because it is not against invading troops, it is not against gangs, it is not *against* a regime that needs overthrowing. It is a Resistance that's not even against anything. Simply being *not in* the thing is enough to get you killed – just like during the war, when German bombing and retaliation caused more civilian casualties in the South than in areas where the Germans were actually being fought.

But I was happy that day. I was happy because I had found someone to take to the wedding of my distant cousin, a wedding I was obliged to attend. I changed clothes in an instant, and I had her wait in a room next to mine. But I locked the door, hoping she wouldn't notice, and I masked the sound of the lock with a fake cough. I considered her a protected species that needed to be kept under lock and key. As we headed across town to the church for the wedding, everyone watched the girl – sidelong glances intended to snare, trying to communicate clearly that if you're not anybody's, you can belong to whoever decides to take you. These glances don't aim to seduce a girl, nor pique her curiosity – they're designed to let off steam, to stroke the girl from afar, because no-one will step up and demand an explanation for the staring. And they want their reward, like the hand of a guy on the bus – hidden beneath a jacket thrown across his forearm – grazing a girl's knee or wrist, often more invasive than a vigorous or explicit grab. These glances stuck to the girl's skin and forced her to look up and down, her eyes darting away; making her sweat more, as if the density of the stares was crowding out all the space and the air in the church. She was a no man's land, and she didn't know it, and I couldn't find the words to let her know that she was considered territory. I managed to drag her into the corner of a side chapel.

And then I started to check the hands of all the grandmothers and aunts, of all the mothers and sisters, of the female cousins and guests. I had to find a wedding ring. I seized my aunt's hand – startling her with my strange lurch of affection – and tried to slide a ring off her finger. But it had been on so long that it wouldn't budge. Tugging did not work, and neither did a splash of holy water. Finally, my grandmother, in her wisdom, took my aunt's finger in her mouth and wetted it with saliva, and the ring then slipped off effortlessly. So I ran back to the side chapel with the wedding band held tight, took the girl's hand, and slid it on. At first she was startled, almost frightened, and then she gazed at me with a honeyed look, as if it were a gift. She hadn't understood at all. I had shielded her. But, once again, I didn't try to explain. Since then, I've always done this, as if the people I love most all needed to be shielded with some symbol, a ring – even though it only remains a shield in some parts of the world; taking her hand and protecting her with a gesture. And to protect myself, as well, as a teenager I started jamming rings on my fingers. One on my left hand, two on my right. Like I saw on the guys from the death squads in the clan. It was a way to tease my mother, to annoy her. Three rings, like the Father, the Son and the Holy Ghost. That is how they wear them where I come from, and that is how I wear them. Meaninglessly, but like the legacy of something that belongs to me without my even knowing why. Something that belongs to my hands. After years of not seeing or hearing from her, I ran into the Northern girl again. This time she is wearing a different ring on her hand. The real kind, a ring that was put on at the right moment, not in a hurry, not in secret. One of those rings that doesn't protect, that doesn't hide, that makes something explicit instead. Or maybe it signifies nothing except the fact of its being gold. She had become a journalist, or something like that. While I'm taking her around on the usual tour of hellish places, she pulls a photo from her bag and shows it to me. A photo – the only photo – of that strange day. But she's not pulling it out to indulge in a moment of nostalgia. The Northern girl, the young woman who has become a journalist, points to two young guys, Giuseppe and Vincenzo, and asks me, "They were killed because they were in the Camorra, right?" Apparently she remembers them from the wedding. She remembers their faces. Anger flares up in you when you least expect it, and you don't know if you can hold back. I could have slapped her face, with the kind of slap that leaves a mark like sunburn, but the very anger itself chokes up my voice and I can't answer, I can't speak. She remembered the guys from the wedding, she remembered them and knew nothing about the event, she knew nothing about them either; all she needed to condemn them was the news of their deaths and some little snippets of information she got over the telephone. A long time has passed since they were killed. Or maybe it's been a short time, but some events you'd like to forget; you'd rather not remember a single detail. Memory, however, doesn't have this power, or at least my memory doesn't. There are places where being born means being guilty. The first newborn breath and the final death rattle have equal value. The value of guilt. It doesn't matter what impulse drove you; it doesn't matter what kind of life you have led. It matters even less what thoughts bounced around your skull, and less still what feelings you acted on, at certain times of day. All that matters is where you were born, what is written on your I.D. card. That place is known only by the people who live there, and guilty people recognize one another. Everyone is guilty, everyone is acquitted. But this place is nothing for those who don't live here.

It was September, the 28th to be precise, an evening when the cold weather seemed slow in coming; the summer was stretched out, almost ready to spread into November. "We'll pay the price for this heat: the winter will be icy!" someone remarked from behind the bar. It was a crappy little sports bar where you could stop for out-of-date soft drinks and brand-new tickets for betting on football matches. The betting tickets were called *la bolletta* – or, to us, *a' bullett*. Betting, gambling, winning a big prize one day, believing you're capable of at least one good thing in your life. Yet that big prize never comes; you only win tiny amounts that are like doses progressively injected into you to keep you betting. And you realize that every win pays half of half of all the years of wasted gambling. In this place, out in front of the little bar where everyone drinks Arnone lemon soda – because Arnone is the local brand and because someone has decreed that only Arnone can be sold – there is a piazza. Everything happens in this piazza. It's always the same timetable, the same faces. Everyone is there, sitting on scooters, sitting on the walls. Joints, beers, chatting. A few scuffles. They are almost all relatives, kids from three, four different families, the same blood, shared memories, the same classes at school. Then there are the new guys, the kids of immigrants, or kids of locals who married immigrant men and women. This place is actually an African country. Not because of the climate, not because of the faux-exotic architecture, but because of the majority of the population living here. This place is inhabited mostly by African immigrants. Not from the Maghreb. Almost all of them are Nigerians,

Senegalese, and many from the Ivory Coast, a few from Sierra Leone, a certain number from Liberia. "There used to be quite a lot more!" says the same someone from behind the counter of the filthy sports bar. Yes, there were more. Meaning, if you saw ten people on the street, nine were African and one was indigenous. And that's assuming you were going by skin colour, because if the one "indigenous" person was Polish, then ten out of ten were immigrants. This place could have been a melting pot of different cultures concentrated in a few square metres. Half of Africa had poured into the streets here, and had broken its back in these tomato fields for seven thousand lire an hour. Nowadays, for five euros. The locals were not cruel to Africans; they weren't contemptuous. On the contrary. Somehow the first joint celebrations began, then a few mixed marriages. Black girls entered the households as babysitters. Over time, however, the powerful people, the truly powerful ones, spread a sense of fear and distrust, and imposed a separation. If contact is really necessary, then it should be minimal, superficial, and momentary. It's every man for himself, and the money just for them. That evening there are five of them. Five of them gulping down lemon sodas and beer. Francesco, Simone, Mirko, Giuseppe and Vincenzo. They're talking. They have always known one another: known one another by sight, gone to some school together, or met on the football pitch for Liternese matches. Maybe they did the army medical check-up together. They talk, laugh, belch. Milan, Turin, Rome. Maps curl around the fragments of conversation of guys from this place. Nobody wants to stay; they feel the guilt. They are growing up, and they sense the guilt of living in this place. Whoever doesn't leave is a failure. They want to make money, but Giuseppe and Vincenzo know that they'll never survive on their work before the age of forty. Giuseppe, twenty-five, is a carpenter. He's good, he has a knack for furniture; it seems he was born to be a cabinetmaker. In his workshop, however, he is still *nu guaglione* – "the boy". He earns a pittance; when he learns the ropes they'll finally pay him a thousand euros a month. Vincenzo is twenty-four and he labours as a bricklayer. Here, work is called "labour". If you don't sweat, if you don't come home with legs that are too stiff to bend, if you don't end the day with a dry mouth and an empty stomach, then you have not "laboured". That's the way the work is. Vincenzo doesn't amount to much as a bricklayer. For now, they have him mixing. He mixes cement, adds water. Once he came to my house along with his *masto*, or boss, to repaint a room that was speckled with damp. He noticed a book here, Ernst Jünger's *The Worker*, and he started joking about it with an intelligence that I did not expect: "Well, I could write a book with a title like that, too; but I'd write the same page over and over: it's always the same here." In the little piazza that night, as always, people talk about much less and about much worse. For too long now, someone has been going back and forth near their little group. Francesco feels someone looking at him. He is twenty-one and building up a career with the people who are in charge. He's tight with the Tavoletta clan. The clan of this place. He deals, and he deals in places where he is not supposed to, but that's why the clan recognizes him as a serious affiliate, even though he is just a kid. He earns one thousand two hundred euros a week. Sometimes he serves as a driver. He has the courage to deal inside the territory of the Tavolettas' enemies, the Bidognetti. Francesco jokes, laughs, drinks his third beer, takes his tenth drag on a joint. But he's not calm. Mirko and Simone are friends. Simone is Giuseppe's brother. They're the ones who first stopped to talk in the piazza, and then the others joined in. That's how groups form in the piazza. They come in waves, they leave in waves. Simone also works in the carpentry workshop. He's the less talented brother, but because he's thirty-one he gets paid more and has the more prestigious tasks; he assembles the cabinetry for newlyweds and spends his time cursing Ikea, which has destroyed people's taste, which allows them to furnish a house for a mere five hundred euros; in the old days, every bride had her obsession, every obsession had its carpenter, and every carpenter got paid. But even the clan – once it sold its land so that Ikea could build its largest European plant – began selling off its carpentry workshops and converting its furniture factories into garages for car mechanics. Mirko is unemployed. His father is finding him a job, maybe up in Formia. Already the idea of Rome excites him. He is thirty-one and he has always worked as a supermarket cashier. Then the supermarket hired a man from Chad who works twice as much for half of Mirko's salary. But Mirko doesn't mind. He lets it go. "It's about time for me to leave," he says to anyone who tries to commiserate. They talk and talk; it's Sunday. There's work tomorrow, dammit. But they go on talking and talking. Francesco pulls out a roll of hundred-euro bills. He's proud. He says that he'll get married before the others and that the wedding will be in Sorrento. The others laugh; they envy him, but they know where that money comes from. The four guys stay away from the clan. Too dangerous, too much effort. Except for Francesco. Meanwhile, those other guys keep going back and forth in the background. This time, Francesco understands. He tries to get away, hurriedly waving goodbye to the group. Vincenzo, Giuseppe, Mirko and Simone don't get it.

The three lookouts who were lurking there in the piazza for hours start racing towards them, pulling out their guns, and the group runs away; Francesco is already ahead of them. The three men have dilated pupils; they're coked up. They're Bidognetti, from the rival clan, sent to punish Francesco. They run, run, loading. They empty two magazines. Smith & Wesson. When shooting with such a heavy weapon, there's no such thing as a good aim: that's just for snipers. All you can do is make a ruckus and alarm people, without hitting any target. The guys manage to escape, they dive into a blind alley; but they'll be alright if they can climb over the wall that separates the road from a small park. Francesco jams his feet into the holes where bricks are missing; he's already on top of the wall. He scaled it in just a few seconds. They fire seven shots at him. Only one hits him, on the collarbone – he doesn't even notice. When you take a bullet at close range, the wound cauterizes immediately, and because of your fear you feel nothing; you only realize in the shower later, when the hot water makes the hole bleed. Francesco drops down on the far side of the wall. He's safe. Mirko and Simone look like two bendy marionettes. They're running breathlessly. They can't stop; they both slam face first into the wall. Hanging on by their finger-nails, they climb the bricks of volcanic stone. Five shots come at them. Mirko gets grazed on the abdomen, Simone on one elbow. Just abrasions, nothing more. They get over the wall. They're safe. The killers are out of breath, choked by cocaine as they try to climb over. They keep falling back; they can't make it. They hear the guys on the other side, running away. People have called the police. But they cannot return empty-handed. Vincenzo and Giuseppe didn't run to the wall. They started knock-ing on several doors. They didn't understand why they were attacked. No-one opens up for them. Even though people know them – even though they know these are the sons of Rosetta and Paola, women the whole town knows – no-one opens up. And yet every-body used to see them as children in the piazza. But they don't open the doors. They don't know who the boys have become now that they're adults. They are hammering on the doors. A couple of retirees open up. Only one couple. They know Giuseppe. In fact, they call him "Peppino". They had him build a wardrobe when their first granddaughter got married. They open their door, the two guys enter. The old couple offer them a glass of water and call the *carabinieri*. They soothe them, trying to understand what has happened in this town they know so well. They would like to say that it has changed completely, that they don't recognize the town they knew when they were young. But they recognize it very well. It has always been like this. Maybe it was even worse before. Around here, the old cliché of the elderly being nostalgic for the way things used to be crumbles pathetically. After a few minutes, though, fresh knocking is heard. The men are kicking the door and hammering at it with the butt of their guns. The guys shout, "What do you want? We're not part of this!" But the Bidognetti men must punish Francesco, and now that he has escaped they must implement the punishment by proxy. Even if it's not Francesco, the bosses will consider the score "evened" if someone close to Francesco is punished – an acquaintance, a neighbour, someone who was talking to him. The Bidognetti clan is called "Midnight", because there's a total blackout over each of their military actions. The Bidognetti men force open the door, the guys try to escape through the kitchen window, but the killers are skilled, and angry. If they go back empty-handed, the clan might dock their salaries for months, and they have families to support. So they pull Vincenzo by his curly hair, and he falls backwards onto the floor. Then they tug his head up, as if they're about to slit a baby goat's throat, but they aim at the nape, at the very top of his neck. With one kick they slam his body, a corpse now, under the table. Giuseppe tries to escape, bouncing off the walls of the tiny room. They take him out with four shots in the belly. He falls into Vincenzo's blood under the table. The old couple don't move. They're not screaming; in fact, they're simply getting ready to step out of their home and tell the *carabinieri* that they walked in and discovered the bloodbath after it happened, that they didn't see anything. It is as if this is yet another thing you're condemned to suffer when you are born into the town of the guilty. The killers hear the sirens. They are the ones who manage to escape through the kitchen window that overlooks the park behind the wall. It's the only escape route. For anybody. The *carabinieri* enter the room. The guys are under the table. On the tablecloth are a peeled tangerine and some spat-out seeds; a knocked-over bottle of *fragolino* wine has seeped into Vincenzo's curly locks. The purple halo on the cloth is perfectly spherical. Sitting in a piazza, running away from fear, being pursued for no reason that you know, by people you've never met. This was Vincenzo and Giuseppe's biggest fault. Innocents. Murdered. Victims not mentioned by any national newspaper the next day. And not by any T.V. news or radio programme. The left wing, the right wing and the centre, all mute. They were all silent. Vincenzo and Giuseppe were born in the town of the guilty. They couldn't claim to be innocent. I should bring her here, the Northern girl: show her the piazza, and tell their story. But I keep looking at her hands, while gripping my anger tight in my own. They are itching like they did many years ago at the station. The wedding ring I had put on her finger, the one now replaced by this new ring that is larger and more beautiful, did not shield her at all; on the contrary, it made me invisible – it made us, this place, this town, invisible. As usual, as always. "They were not in the Camorra," I would like to reply, "they were Partisans." Perhaps it would be too rhetorical, but better than a slap in the face; but once again she would not understand. Now Giuseppe's mother spends her days in the road, on a chair, near the sports bar. She asks anyone who catches her eye, "Would you go and call Giuseppe for me? He always stays out late at night . . . he has to work tomorrow." "I'll go and call him for you," people say, and then they hasten on their way. She stares after them for as long as her myopia allows, until the person disappears around a corner. And then she slowly turns her head back, lowers it, and continues to wait.

# THE OPPOSITE
# OF DEATH

I imagine it as a place covered with sand, full of mountains topped with snow. Sand and snow together. Although sand and snow don't mix – they never mingle in anyone's dreams. But I always imagine dust, sand, markets swept by the wind, the same wind we have on our beaches here. And in the distance, the snow on the mountain peaks. And then turbans, many beards. And those clothes that swallow you up, that seem even beautiful to me. Clothes you wear when you don't want to be seen, when you want to be nothing more than fabric. At times I would like to wear them here, when I feel everyone's eyes glued to my face. If I smile, I'm smiling too much and I've forgotten him already; and if my eyes are swollen with tears, they mutter that I should pull myself together, as crying won't bring him back; and if I show no emotion at all they're already passing judgement: "She's gone mad with grief." And I wish I could hide myself under those blue bells, inside those burqas.

Maria closes her eyes and tries to picture Afghanistan. She takes some images that have passed through her mind in all these days and she describes them to me. It is the first time she's doing this with a stranger. But maybe I'm the only one who feels that I'm a stranger; maybe she saw me in church during the funeral, or perhaps she recalls seeing me when I came to play football around these parts, or came to the gym posing as a boxer and pretending to vent my feelings by pounding the punchbag. She speaks to me of a land she's never seen, but it is as if she knows every image broadcast by the T.V., every picture that's appeared in the newspapers: it's as if she has trained her eye to catch every detail behind the shoulder of each journalist reporting from Kabul, or in the articles in the women's weeklies that are packed with photographs.

Afghanistan has become a land that she mentions every day, more than she mentions the name of her own town. It's always right in front of her. It's a strange name – hard to pronounce; in her dialect it's twisted into Affanìstan, Afgrànistan, Afgà. And around here the name is linked not with Bin Laden or the Taliban, but chiefly with Afghani hashish – the best kind there is, the kind that came through here in small bars like gold ingots and that filled the garages, and that was for years the true attraction for everyone in the local drug-dealing piazzas.

Maria is almost obsessed with Afghanistan. It's not an obsession that she chose for herself. It's a neurosis that she was unlucky enough to discover inside herself. The people close to her avoid any words that could even remotely remind her of the sounds of the word "Afghanistan". As if a simple sound could suffice to revive her pain or remind her for a moment, afresh, of the origin of her pain: "Afghanistan", as if she could ever forget even for a moment. Maria notices these unnecessary kindnesses. At first she was annoyed, the same way you get annoyed by those men who obligingly open doors with too much attentiveness or who apologize when using words unsuited for feminine ears. That's just false good manners, which serve to showcase the tact and subtlety of the noble seducer rather than expressing consideration for the person on the receiving end.

Maria cannot forget. She can't not think about it. It wasn't very long ago, but not even for one afternoon can she keep from thinking about what happened, and where it happened, and wondering what could have been done to avoid it. She wonders, which you should never do. They train you, here, to consider everything that happens as inevitable. It's not the ancient fatalism that means accepting everything with open arms and bended knees. The daily training in taking everything as it comes, here, leads towards an attitude that's even more invasive. If it happened, you must try to turn it to your advantage – and this attitude prevents you from understanding.

Understanding how things work, how things can be avoided, and where things come from. It's like taking every day as the worst one possible, but understanding how to profit from each one. Just a wretched little advantage that can wring some benefit from Destiny's moment of distraction, from a brief pause as the landslide crashes down on you.

No-one around Maria was asking how and why it happened. Everything happens just because it must. You just endure, and squeeze whatever you can out of what you must endure. You get what you can from whatever hits you, but you can never decide what alms you're permitted to request from the misfortune, what you deserve and why you deserve it. And the anger and pain seem to be born at the moment when you realize that you cannot find any benefit in it.

But Maria is sick with questions. She asks the soldiers who were in Kabul with Enzo, and who have been back here for a while now; she asks anyone who is back for just a short leave. She asks anyone coming back from the latest war. She asks questions that she manages to jam in amid the bouquet of heartfelt and thoughtful words that they offer her as the widow, as the bride who stumbled before she even reached the altar. In town, there are veterans from every war, from all the recent wars. Veterans from those recent wars that aren't called battles or conflicts anymore, but "missions". Peace missions. Around here, though, the relatives, the village kids, the girlfriends and the brothers all call them simply: "the latest war".The latest war tosses the previous wars further back into the past. The latest war had been Iraq, a few months ago; for a long time before that, the latest war was Bosnia. Now, the latest war for people around here is Afghanistan. But everyone from the town of Casavatore, and from all the way over to Villaricca, on the other hand, went to Nasiriyah; and for the people inland, Lebanon is now the latest war. The soldiers left for Lebanon only a few months ago, but they are not mentioned. There are no shootings, no protest marches, no live video link-ups with T.V. shows that save families the cost of a phone call, no wives going on camera to show that the rounded little belly he left at home has ballooned hugely. So the fictional place is constructed out of JPEGs sent by the soldiers from the front in e-mails that serve to empty out their cameras' memory cards, and to back up the pictures to display to their girls and to show their families where they are working, and how they're getting by.

Newspapers do not want photos of ordinary days spent on the front lines. Army patrols, babies being carried, guys sitting on tanks with legs dangling, sunglasses and machine guns. They're all too predictable, or simply a daily report on wars that mustn't seem too everyday for anyone. Video is wanted, but only if you shoot at people who are wounded, only if you curse the enemy, only if you violate the rules of engagement, or if some enemy pounces and you're filmed while they're gutting you. When the little kids from around here go on to school in Naples, or when they follow their fathers' and mothers' deployments to various barracks and end up in school in Rome or Turin, they don't understand when the new class talks about "the latest war".

They're thinking of the wars where their fathers were or where their brothers are now, and they rack their brains to remember if that war is really the latest one, and to figure out if this is really what's being asked. And then they say: "The latest war was in Kosovo, 1999, my father was there," or "The latest war was in Afghanistan." The rest of the class almost always burst out laughing – smirking because nothing is easier to answer than "What was the latest war?" They're not asking you about the Triple Alliance, or the year when the Armistice was signed after the First World War. They're just asking about the latest war – the easiest thing there is. Only a fool could get that wrong.

For the kids from my neighbourhood, though, layers and layers of other wars stand between the latest war they know and the latest war they're taught about in school. The earliest remembered war doesn't have Nazi uniforms and liberators' helmets; it's Lebanon in 1982 and the "Italcon" or Italian Contingent. But this isn't historical memory – no-one reads a book to remember this; it's simply a bar-stool memory: stories you tell while cursing the bank for refusing to defer your mortgage payments, or while unwrapping the new calendar that the army sends you each year.

If you say "veteran" and "the last war" elsewhere in Italy, you're flooded with images of grey-haired heroines of the anti-Fascist Resistance. But this place is full of veterans who are very young. Veterans who are raring to redeploy, veterans who come home and invest all their earnings in a bar. Or they open a restaurant with their comrades in arms – they begin by splashing out on marble countertops and chefs and then, almost always, things start going sour. And then they deploy again to the front somewhere, if they're still the right age, if they haven't taken a hasty discharge, if they've kept up the right contacts that can get them a posting. Civilian armed security guard teams all across Italy are full of veterans because – after you have escorted a food convoy and defended it from K.L.A. guerrillas or from Aidid's troops – you can escort a junior minister or a government witness without dreaming every night that you're getting blown up.

The majority of the troops on missions are soldiers from the South. More than half of the Italian war dead are from the South. This province is full of veterans. Soldiers who have returned from Bosnia, and from Mozambique before that; soldiers back from Kosovo, soldiers back from Somalia, soldiers back from Iraq, soldiers back from Lebanon or awaiting a return to Lebanon. Soldiers who sent back only their bodies, burned and lacerated and dismembered.

It's full of soldiers here. Paratroopers from the Folgore brigade, riflemen from the Garibaldi brigade, paratrooper carabinieri from the Tuscania regiment, as well as the Alpini mountain infantry, and the San Marco battalion, and the Sassari mechanized brigade. There's hardly anyone around here who hasn't thought of enlisting, at least once. Only if you were born without a kidney or with a club foot; only if you have retinitis pigmentosa that will blind you, then no: those are the only obstacles that keep people from yearning to join the army. And people apply anyway, even in those cases. People try; it's up to the military doctors to discover the problem. People hope for a moment of distraction – for a deaf and blind doctor. Around here, even one-legged guys would try to enlist. And although in the old days of conscription thousands of young guys got themselves exempted because of fictitious anal fistulas, or paid a fortune for a cup of blood-contaminated urine as a sample that would ensure they would be ruled unfit, this no longer holds, now that "army" means a job and salary.

Where I come from, the place to register for enlistment is at the service counter of a barracks facing the Royal Palace of Caserta. They come in dozens of cars and, since it's a tourist spot, they park far away and then, carrying a thermos full of coffee, wrapping themselves in blankets, they queue all night to be the first to hand in an application the next day. After the law abolishing the draft, the volunteers feel unlucky; they would have happily taken advantage of the lax rules from that era that would have counted them fit to serve. Conscientious objection was a choice for left-wing guys who could spend that whole year not earning anything – almost all of them were students. For others, however, it was a year of lost earnings, and the draft was an opportunity, a chance to test whether barracks and uniforms were better than the construction site and the tool shop, better than driving trucks halfway across Europe, or working behind a bar.

All of Maria's relatives have enlisted or tried to enlist, and Maria knows all the veterans' wives and girlfriends. Besides, not knowing these women would mean that she spent no time with her peers.

"They can't help it: they always ask me weird things, like 'How do you know if they've sent your husband to a dangerous place?', or 'What do they tell you before letting you know about the death?' They want to protect themselves, to know so they won't be caught by surprise, to learn from a friend who has had misfortune – like a vaccination, to understand it immediately, or to try to avoid it. All my friends who have boyfriends off at war want me to tell my story. When I finish, they ask me to tell it again, and after that they ask me to tell it over again. 'Let it all out!' they say, but the truth is that they don't want to miss a single detail. And the more they listen to me and look at me, the more they fear ending up like me. So they try to understand everything, and I can already picture them going home and e-mailing their boyfriends to tell them to do the exact opposite of what Enzo did."

Maria appears to be wise beyond her years. She got it somewhere, from the distillation of identical moments she's living through, where the minutes seem to run on longer than the years she has lived, minutes colliding with each other, pressing together in this life of hers that no longer has the breadth it should have.

"These women don't understand that these things can't be decided by others. Where their boy-friends will go, what they'll do. They are commanded. And their own lives don't depend on them. But how can I explain that? They believe that listening to me will help them save their boyfriends – and why shouldn't I let them believe it?"

Maria's hands are sweaty, and she twists them together. We decide to walk through the town; no-one is watching us. Or rather, everyone is used to always seeing Maria with someone by her side, as if it were an addition to the comfort of her family. She looks like a child, especially her feet. They're fitted with little shoes that I'm sure she bought in a children's shop – the size is too small, a size you can't find in shops for adults. And the style is doll-like, with four cut-out holes on the top of the foot. She wears her hair in layers, with two clips at the temples that keep it from falling in her eyes. Her nose is pointed, like a little blade stuck between her cheeks. She wears black tights, a big black sweater and a black jacket. She has no make-up. There's something oriental about her eyes, perhaps because they are in such perfect harmony with her petite, almost porcelain body. She already has a widow's mask. She seems like a miraculously youthful version of her grandmothers, of her mother. Sometimes when she's dressed in dark clothes like this – and occasionally she even wears a black kerchief on her head – it's laughable: she looks as if she's pretending. Like a little girl in front of the mirror, with her feet swimming around inside her mother's shoes, with huge necklaces hanging from her skinny neck to her navel. That's what Maria seems like – a caricature of her grandmothers in their permanent mourning clothes. She and all the women in her family have been dressed in black for months now. Soon it will be a whole year. An ever-lasting mourning that does not end. The mourning for Enzo occasionally includes some other young man who drops dead, gets killed, passes on. And the guy generates mourning that extends to everyone: neighbours, friends, aunts, distant cousins. In my town, all my aunt's friends always dressed in black, because there was always a boy who had been killed, a distant relative falling from some scaffold; because respect always had to be shown for some family that had lost someone. And when there was nothing to mourn, they continued to wear black because soon, surely, there would be something. So you might as well never take it off. When someone in his sixties dies – someone old – when someone dies of illness, close relatives can be the only ones wearing mourning; but when a young man dies, then it must be everyone. Like a shared burden, or a misfortune from which there is no escape.

Where I come from, when someone dies in war, everyone in the apartment building dresses in black. As a child I would look forward to baptisms and to Christmas when I could see the women of my house dressed in something other than black. Baptisms meant that they had to wear another colour, and Christmas required red. But my aunt was embarrassed: she was so used to black that she wore dark colours anyway; she couldn't see herself in bright colours. Once I blurted out: "Black even at Christmas, dammit – who died?"

"No, no, can't you see? This is blue."

In Maria's house, too, all the women were in black. Maria invites me in. Her room is just as I expected. Still the same as when she was little. Posters, oversized cuddly toys, even a display case with one of those super-luxury collectors' edition

Barbie dolls that parents prevented you from playing with – just for show. A room that she expected to leave behind when she moved to a house, as a married woman, but where she is now trapped as a widow. On the computer there's a small picture, the kind you buy in San Gregorio Armeno: the Gulf of Naples lit by small lights that represent the rush of lava. A small object that makes something beautiful out of the time-worn postcard cliché iconography. Naples seems so far away from this town. I ask her about the computer. As I imagined, she bought it because of Enzo's departure for Afghanistan.

"We had one e-mail account, and no-one knew the password except for us two. Enzo was jealous: he was afraid that I'd write to someone I met in a chat room. But I downloaded the software to chat with him – with no-one but him." Perhaps she's lying, but she's right to lie. All the girls around here bought computers when their boyfriends left. For e-mailing, and chatting when they were both online. Free or almost free communication. Ever since the military bases got computer centres, the number of internet contracts and broadband connections shot up around here. The local technician who installs the Fastweb routers is a veteran who was in Somalia; he learned how to use wires and screwdrivers in the Folgore brigade. And whenever he can, he always goes to the homes of soldiers' girlfriends first; he tries to prioritize their needs, as if a remnant of warrior's honour keeps him feeling as if he's a member of a community of fighters.

In Maria's room there are pictures of Enzo everywhere. Enzo at the beach. Enzo training in the gym. Enzo kissing her. There's a very sweet one that makes me laugh: Enzo holding her up in the air with both hands, horizontally, like a dumb-bell, the kind used by Olympic weightlifters. Enzo was not muscular. He had the athletic body of someone who will become a boxer, but a flyweight.

And then a picture with the Colosseum behind them. The classic tourist tour of Rome.

"Yes, that's just before he left for Afghanistan. The first time I went to Rome. We went to see the shops selling the most beautiful wedding favours, the least tacky ones, the ones that aren't used by everyone; and then at home in our town we were going to look for the ones most like the Roman ones." Maria's friends, the ones who went to college, had said she would make a great impression if, instead of giving out wedding favours, she gave out lapel pins for Emergency, the N.G.O. for war victims. Emergency operated in Afghanistan too, and – who knows? – maybe somewhere in Kabul Enzo would meet that doctor with the white beard, Gino Strada.

"I really did consider that Emergency thing. But can you imagine all my relatives? They would not get it – that little bow, and that badge; they couldn't have put it on the shelf at home along with the wedding favours from all the other family weddings. They would have thought that my family couldn't even afford favours for their daughter's wedding."

Maria pauses frequently when she's talking about these things. She must be careful not to lose herself. It is risky: often she gets lost chasing memories and cannot find the breath to speak, suffocating on everything that didn't happen. Like a fish pulled from the aquarium. Choked by oxygen.

She manages to tell me about that morning. She had returned home with the wedding favours, chosen on her own, but identical to the Roman ones she had seen with Enzo; she had not yet bought the dress but she had already tried on three, and she had her eye on one in particular.

"My brother answered the phone; it was Enzo's mother; he called out to me. He was still on the phone with her when he told me that Enzo had been wounded, that the Taliban had attacked a truck, a tank with Enzo inside. But Enzo was not in any tanks or trucks; he had never sent me any photographs where he was close to the tanks.

"They told me right away, so I didn't get scared immediately. I had no saliva in my mouth, but my brother continued talking to Enzo's mother and so I thought that it wasn't serious. I figured that people give you bad news gradually. That the carabinieri car would have gone to Enzo's mother's place, and then his father would have told my father, and my father would have called me in there, into the living room, where people bring you in to tell you terrible things, saying, 'I must talk to you, Maria,' and in the meantime I would have realized that something serious had happened. Instead, while I was just sorting out the wedding favours, my brother – still on the phone – mumbled the news to me. Who could have expected it? I didn't get scared right away. We turned on the television, but there was nothing; we looked on the internet – nothing. We phoned the numbers we had, Enzo's friends, but no-one knew, nobody said anything. The first news I got from T.V.; then they called us and told us that Enzo had been in an armoured vehicle outside Kabul, and that his vehicle had driven over a landmine and the mine had exploded and the vehicle upended and that someone died, but that Enzo made it."

In fact, what blew up the armoured vehicle was not a simple anti-tank mine but a remote control; the Taliban had been waiting for an Italian convoy to pass before they triggered the bomb. In the armoured vehicle were four soldiers. It flipped right over. The soldiers' eardrums popped immediately, plunging them into silence. Enzo had no legs: the wounds were cauterized immediately, the femoral artery was closed off, and the armoured vehicle went up in flames. The fire went right out, as if to make him suffer even more: the vehicle suddenly became a furnace, and they had exploded eardrums, and metal plates like flying scimitars were cutting right through everything. The explosion sent one soldier against the roof of the vehicle, breaking his neck instantly; two others survived; Enzo's body was half in and half out.

The Taliban had blown up the convoy. The armoured car hadn't protected anything. It was cut open from beneath, and splinters rained inside.

"We were told he could be saved, that's what they told us . . ."

In the village, people immediately began to make banners to welcome him home; the family couldn't leave the house without everyone asking – they all wanted to know about Enzo.

"Even the bank manager – the one who hadn't

wanted to give us a loan because we couldn't give guarantees – even this guy, who was one of the reasons why Enzo had done the maths and had gone to war, he kept coming up to my mother and saying: 'A loan for the kids – count on me as soon as the caporale gets back; as soon as the caporale gets back, come to me!' I wanted to spit in his face, but a woman doesn't do such a thing." When he landed in Rome from the Kabul flight, they took him to the hospital. The town almost celebrated; people had even bought fireworks, and the best pyrotechnicians in the area were ready to do a show for free. It felt festive. But there was no homecoming. Enzo died. Perhaps after the attack there was just one last breath in his lungs, just enough so the first bulletin could report that he was not dead; enough air that they could avoid breaking the news of too many front-line deaths. And they spread out the death reports, one at a time, one a week. "I realized he was dead from how my mother approached me. She hugged me; it had been years since my mother had hugged me. She hugged me and started to run her fingers through my hair, because she knew there was always a lull before I reacted to something. In no time at all I had destroyed everything I saw, including the television – I threw the wedding favours off the balcony; I did not want anything to survive Enzo. Not even things. Not even me."

Maria insisted that she wanted to see him, she had to see him, she had a right to see him. But the bodies of the war dead could not be displayed. Even death has its protocol. The war dead cannot be seen by those who do not know war's ferocity. And Maria's family believed she should not approach a shattered body. Enzo was there, on a table in a military hospital in Rome. Like all the dead. In a room identical to other rooms in millions of hospitals, where they all end up, just like all other morgues, whiteness and tiles and the smell of disinfectant. There was little, too little of him. Enzo's brother had seen him, had identified him, but could not touch him: just one kiss on his forehead risked peeling off the skin that had remained stuck to the bone. Maria insisted. She wanted to see him, she wanted to be with him one last time. But she could not see him like this. So they made a pact, one of those pacts that you extort from people who are powerless – with their swollen eyes and filled with mucus from weeping – but who are firm in their intentions. Enzo's brother let her go into the morgue with her eyes covered. He had one hand in Maria's right hand and the other over her eyes. That other hand that could prevent Maria's curiosity from prising open her eyelids for even a moment. That's the way he brought her close to the table, close to Enzo. "I don't know how he came back, I didn't see what they did to him. I smelled a terrible odour, like chicken skin when it's burned. But that was not his smell. I felt that he was there and I felt him beside me. I felt that something had been saved. It was as if I had entered a room that he was in."

Maria gripped Enzo's brother's hand so tightly that her nails, long and manicured like those of a woman about to get married, sank into his palm. But Enzo's brother said nothing about it, or he didn't feel it.

Enzo had enlisted in the army with the specific

intention of being sent on missions. He had stopped going to the gym, where he was one of the best boxers. People believe that guys enlist for the money. And, too often, people use the word "mercenary". Mercenary. It sounds good, strong, fierce; it sounds crucial enough. It has an air of romantic inspiration. A fighter should fight not for money but for love of a country. What a joke. And guys from around here don't even take offence when they're arguing and the other guys their age insult them by calling them "mercenaries". It's hard to see why soldiers are the only ones who shouldn't consider the pay for their work. When they go on missions, their pay is tripled, sometimes even quadrupled. But then there's all the rest of it. The rest of it is the chance to grow, to do something that has the weight of respectability, of a commitment, of the annual bonus, of vacation time, of being valued as someone, a person to be considered. And the chance to see a bit of the world. And, for some, to see what it's like to make war, to shoot and get shot at. To invade, strike, challenge. But for many it's just going and getting back as soon as possible, all in one piece. And bringing some pictures home with them.

Soldiers from different wars. Southern Italy is the leader in violent deaths for young people. As she told me about her blind reunion, Maria's cheekbones were wet with tears. But she stopped crying almost immediately. As if she had decided to stem the tidal wave starting to rise.

The first time I saw her she was embracing a coffin, on her knees. In church. Small, she was smaller than she is in now, right in front of me. I feel like I'm seeing her again. To suppress her memories, Maria gets some water and starts to drink. The water drips from the corners of her mouth. Everything about her seems silently hungry. Hunger, thirst, sleepiness. Everything seems to be a sign of life, a life that pulsates under her skin, but like a fuel that does not permit her to switch off, not even for a moment. Doesn't permit her to surrender. Maria makes a gesture, a lovely gesture, the kind you don't forget once you've seen it close up, and you can feel your blood flowing through you. It is a gesture that my mother always made when she felt hot. A gesture that people make in the country. They dip their fingers in the trace of water at the bottom of their drinking glass and then slide their fingers down their chest, right between the breasts, where the sweat doesn't run easily, like a quick rinse. The gesture must be instinctive, because it is just as insolent as picking your nose or removing a piece of meat stuck between your teeth.Yet it's done so naturally. At that moment I see the pendant that Maria is wearing. Not a cross, nor a zealot's religious charm; not a saint's portrait, nor a holy rosary. But Enzo's dogtag. Deformed by the fire and the heat. And I'm reminded of a scene from Enzo's funeral. All his boxing friends from the gym had their hands bandaged, all of them in the front pews of the church. When the time came for Communion, they didn't line up in front of the priest; only the old ladies lined up, while all the guys – military and non-military, veterans, fellow soldiers – took hold of their dog-tags. Each one of them had a dogtag. They scooped them from their chests and at the very instant when the priest lifted the Host and offered it to the old ladies, the guys put their own metal Host into their mouths. I looked around. Everyone was doing it. I picked up my own dogtag and pressed it between my teeth. I wear a dogtag and it feels like I've worn it since birth. It is a military dogtag; it's got my first name, surname, date and place of birth, blood type and a sentence from Terence in Latin. Just enough to identify me, enough to synthesize what I am: to carry myself in written form on my own chest. Everyone or almost everyone I know has a dogtag, a dangling metal biography. It's like a stylistic feature of youth on the outskirts of cities, a provocation, a declaration of a permanent state of metropolitan conflict. As if there's a need to feel like soldiers at all times, even without an army, hating war and loving combat. Actually, the dogtag is a key factor in understanding my land, my country, my people. One of my class-mates from lower secondary school, Salvatore, was identified thanks to his dogtag.

Salvatore worked as an "escort", to help trucks brimming unbelievably with drugs to avoid checkpoints. The trucks stuffed with cocaine or hashish almost always travel with two decoy cars that monitor the roads they'll take, alerting them to roadblocks or the presence of police cars and carabinieri. If there is a roadblock, the driver decides to leave the highway for several kilometres, and if that's impossible, a car comes into play that's called "the Wreck" in some neighbourhoods: a beat-up car that accompanies important shipments, always keeping a slight distance, and when needed it approaches the checkpoints driving conspicuously and dangerously so that it gets stopped, permitting the shipment to pass undisturbed. Salvatore was a "Wreck" driver. He became famous because when he was escorting a truck and couldn't get himself stopped at the checkpoint, he didn't consider his mission a failure; instead he would rear-end a random car on purpose, deliberately causing an accident, so that the emergency would dissolve the roadblock and send the police cars to the disaster. Things ended badly for Salvatore. He went off the road after deliberately slamming into a jeep. His car caught fire, but not completely, and so the flames enveloped him slowly; the motor burned and black smoke filled the car. When the firefighters arrived, Salvatore was completely burned. But they could immediately identify him because he wore a dogtag. He wore one, like everyone else. Name, surname, date and place of birth, and blood group. And on the back, his girl-friend's name. An addition to his metal biography.

Now doctors, firemen and policemen always reach for the chest, feeling around with their hands for a dogtag, to avoid checking pockets, pulling out I.D. cards, or asking the dying, "What's your name?" And when they don't find a dogtag, it is as if they're dealing with a novice, like some youngster who didn't put on a helmet, or the imprudence of someone who wanders unprepared through a war zone. The dogtag is a drag – it's uncomfortable. Every time you hug someone in the cold, this little postage stamp gives off a shock if it touches the other person's skin, and in the summer it sticks to your chest with sweat, and when you make love it dangles against the girl's nose or even drops into her mouth. Every one of my friends has shown off the bite marks that they claim their women have put onto their dogtags; I always squinted at the metal and never saw anything but microscopic scratches. Every scratch comes from a different female canine tooth, according to their tales.

A dogtag is a trace. The trace of a country at war. Of part of a country at war. A country at war that doesn't know it's at war. Of men burning on different fronts. Burning like Salvatore or like Enzo.

While we're talking and I'm trying to soften the embarrassment by showing her my dogtag, Maria leaps up and grabs a colourful dress out of the closet. She shows it to me. And amid all the dimness of clothes and shadow, it shines at me like a flashlight pointed straight at my eyes. We're three days away from her birthday. The dress that Maria will wear to her party is what she was planning to wear on the day they were to sign their wedding paperwork. I realize I don't know her age. I've always taken it for granted that she was generically young. I ask: "How old are you?"

Maria looks at me, swallows. Perhaps no-one asks her this question anymore, in recent months.

"Seventeen; eighteen in three days."

I think I've misheard her.

"Seventeen."

Enzo was twenty-one. Soldiers almost never have a specific age. When they are not considered killers, or ferocious, they're all generically young. But when their youth is cut short with a death notice, dying at twenty-one is too young even for a volunteer soldier who went to Afghanistan to pay for his wedding and the down payment on a house. And when you say the age out loud, the distance – from the event, from the uniform, from the duty, from the distant land – collapses and slams you right on the nose. That "seventeen", said so simply, the way people state their age, hit me like a glass door that you walk right into because it's so transparent. I had thought she looked like a child, and she was a child. She is a child. A child widow. A bride in white. Seventeen years old. It feels as if I'm gazing at something sacred. A kind of archetypal recurring image, a tragic Vestal from some historical period. The young girls widowed by young boy soldiers. Girls who became completely untouchable because they were always guarded by the spectres of their prospective husbands. That's what I was looking at. It tempts you to mouth the usual secular platitudes you overhear on the bus, that you hear on the political talk shows: that everything stays the same, that nothing changes, that there's no difference between past and present. But Maria herself blocks that temptation. We go back out, and she brings me to the bar downstairs. It is full of veterans. It was started by a former paratrooper from the Folgore brigade. He had been in Somalia and then got embroiled in some story about turtles being set under tank treads by soldiers, and he took off, leaving the bar to his wife. Tommaso is there, glued to the video poker machine. He was in the war in Bosnia and he hates soldiers from any other mission. He spends a fortune on poker. He loses everything there is to lose on it. And he wins just often enough to motivate him to keep playing. Maria wants me to talk to him, or at least meet him. Tommaso is one of the angriest veterans, one who has had no peace since he returned.

"Nowadays the guys' camps are like Club Med; when we went, we shat ice in open fields; we had no satellite link-ups; when we wrote to our families we had to send postcards. Now they have gyms and the internet, and they're never let out of the barracks. What do they know about Sarajevo, about Bulevar Selimovica Mese – what was called 'Sniper Alley'? They would have shit their pants. What do they know about M.R.U.D.s or PROM-1 mines? They know nothing about that. Nowadays they go just to parade around; we were really at war." Tommaso hates other veterans, the ones who weren't in Bosnia like him. He always comes to stir up trouble with soldiers just returning from some mission; he hates the Iraq veterans most of all, because they have Nasiriyah, the symbol of that massacre, the memory of that sacrifice. And he wants his soldiers to be remembered, as if all the other massacres were minor compared to his. Tommaso has troubled dreams; Maria would like to help, but Tommaso is not approachable. They say he keeps dreaming about the house-to-house patrol in Sarajevo where watches with gold wristbands were dangling from dresser drawers. As soon as the drawer was opened and the watch lifted out, everything blew up. It was a trap: the drawer was connected directly to a mine. A young guy got blown up right in front of him. A young guy he had ordered to go and fetch the watch. But these are just stories that people tell about him. He speaks to no-one about his dreams. The only obvious thing about Tommaso is his terror about his health – he's a hypochondriac. He's just waiting his turn, but he's sure that sooner or later it will come. Tommaso is terrified that he might father deformed children, sick from his contact with depleted uranium. So terrified that he doesn't want children; so terrified that his wife has filed for divorce. Maria provokes him to get him to fly into a rage; she wants me to see the pain on Tommaso's face.

"So many are dead . . ."

"Worse than death. I've counted fifty-eight cases so far: twenty-four dead from thyroid cancer, twenty-one dead with their balls rotten and thirteen dead from Hodgkin's lymphoma. I wish my memory didn't work so well. How many dead then? More in Nasiriyah? – or more in Bosnia and Kosovo?" Tommaso was Enzo's friend, but Maria discovered this only a few days ago.

"It's strange, I realize that I know so little about Enzo. I haven't got anything left because they didn't give us enough time to make memories; they didn't give us enough time to have a past. We had only what happened, and nothing more. Once they took him away, they took everything from me. Someone should have told me that that's how it worked. That I had nothing yet . . . but I was getting ready to have something. And just when I was having it, I no longer had it."

Maria is left with wedding announcements and packets of invitations; she's left with whole parts of life that were designed and laid out, but that never became real.

"Of all the years we spent together, I have so little left; I know that he liked orange juice in the morning; that when he went to pick peaches at Villa Literno he would come home with a stomach ache because he would eat pounds of them. I know he loved Pietro Aurino, the boxer from Torre Annunziata; whenever Aurino had a match, Enzo would hitch a ride from the truckers who were his father's friends, to go and see it. I know that he liked to sleep with me, and that he wanted to leave this town, but here we could buy a house and all our people were here. I know that he was embarrassed to kiss me in front of his family. I know that I liked it when he scolded me out of his absurd jealousy, because if too many guys looked at me it meant that I was dressed in the wrong way. I know about the photos he sent me from Kabul, I know he liked the markets, he used to say that the locals didn't seem aggressive at all; he wrote that he wanted to take me to Afghanistan someday, and that everyone in Kabul was tired of war, and that everyone just wished for peace, like them. He wrote that he never expected the country to be so beautiful that it almost made you want to live there and to curse whoever had destroyed it. I know that he photographed the mountains for me. He said that when he was totally fed up, he could find silence wherever he needed it. Which he could never do at home. But there are many things I still don't know, that I still haven't found, that I have yet to discover, to understand, to learn about him."

She still doesn't know. It's as if Enzo lives on, as if he's not finished. As if there's still time. Maria is convinced that he lives on, that it's still possible to make what Enzo was continue.

"Do you remember Carmela?" she asks, and hard as I try, I can't recall any girl with that name. Then it becomes clear. "If love is the opposite of death" are words from Sergio Bruni's "Carmela", one of the most beautiful songs ever written. The lyrics by the old singer from Villaricca trounce hundreds of verses by the greatest poets. Maria is certain. She can keep him from death – tear him away from death. She can do it, if she continues to love him enough. Like a reverse Eurydice who can hope to bring Orpheus out from the perimeter of Hades only if she doesn't take her eyes off him. A Eurydice who cannot get sidetracked, who doesn't want to take her eyes off Orpheus for even a moment.

Saying the word "love" is embarrassing. The tongue halts, as if it's tired of travelling a worn path, a path too often travelled, that it no longer wants to take. It's like a sound that is too well known. Like the phrases people chant without regard to meaning. Or like prayers that possess a sacredness that loses all content, with only the ritual remaining. There is a moment, however, when a word that's been slobbered by too many mouths, manipulated and distended by too many careless hands, becomes immaculate. There's no understanding why; one cannot backtrack and do it again. It just happens.

Hearing Maria whispering those lyrics, I felt I understood everything at last, as if she had taught me the most valuable of lessons, a lesson for which I had searched so far – down at the bottom of the barrel of words, in the metaphysics of theorems – while I actually had it right here, simple and solved. Pawing through a basket of thoughts and aphorisms, I had found unsatisfactory answers that did nothing to help me understand. And now every time I have no knowledge, every time I lack a definition, every time I fail to grasp a conclusive meaning – now I know the truth of love. It's the only truth that is still heard and understood in your very being: the opposite of death.

ROBERTO SAVIANO writes for *La Repubblica* and newspapers around the world. After the success of *Gomorrah* he received death threats and has been forced to live in hiding since 2006. He has been the recipient of the European Book Award, the PEN/Pinter Award and the Olof Palme Prize for his stance against organised crime and corruption. The film adaptation of *Gomorrah* won the 2008 Grand Jury Prize in Cannes. Also published in English is his collection of essays, *Beauty and the Inferno* (MacLehose Press, 2011).

ABIGAIL ASHER is an editor and translator who has worked in publishing in both Milan and New York.

Roberto Saviano

# BEAUTY & THE INFERNO

*Translated from the Italian by Oonagh Stransky*

The writings collected in *Beauty and the Inferno* tackle universal themes
with great insight and humanity, with urgency, and often with anger.

The breadth of Saviano's interests is remarkable, his heroes as diverse
as Donnie Brasco and Lionel Messi, but as with the bestselling *Gomorrah*,
his fearless and unflinching condemnation of the Italian mafia takes
centre stage. Implicit in his tributes to writers, musicians,
sportsmen and journalists is the message that there is an alternative
to living in corruption and fear.

*Beauty and the Inferno* is a searing polemic that encompasses
Saviano's vision of life and of art, celebrating the good to be found
in humanity and calling out the evil inherent to power. Above all, his
commitment to truth resonates from every page.

## MACLEHOSE PRESS

www.maclehosepress.com
*Subscribe to our quarterly newsletter.*